Original Film Tracks

Wise Publications
London/New York/Sydney

Exclusive Distributors:

Music Sales Limited
8/9 Frith Street,
London W1V 5TZ, England.

Music Sales Pty Limited
120 Rothschild Avenue,
Rosebery, NSW 2018, Australia.

This book © Copyright 1990
by Wise Publications

Order No. AM71994

UK ISBN 0.7119.1543.1

Art direction by Mike Bell
Design by Carroll, Dempsey & Thirkell
Compiled by Peter Evans

Printed in the United Kingdom by
Dotesios Printers Limited, Trowbridge, Wiltshire.

Music Sales complete catalogue
lists thousands of titles and is free
from your local music shop, or
direct from Music Sales Limited.
Please send £1 in stamps for postage to
Music Sales Limited, 8/9 Frith Street,
London W1V 5TZ.

Arthur's Theme
(Best That You Can Do)

Words & Music by Burt Bacharach, Carole Bayer Sager,
Christopher Cross & Peter Allen

Once in your life, you'll find
Ar - thur, he does what he

self,   hey,   what-'ve I found?
way   they   want him to be.

When you get caught be-tween the moon and New York Cit - 'y,

I know it's cra - zy,   but it's true.___

If you get caught be - tween the

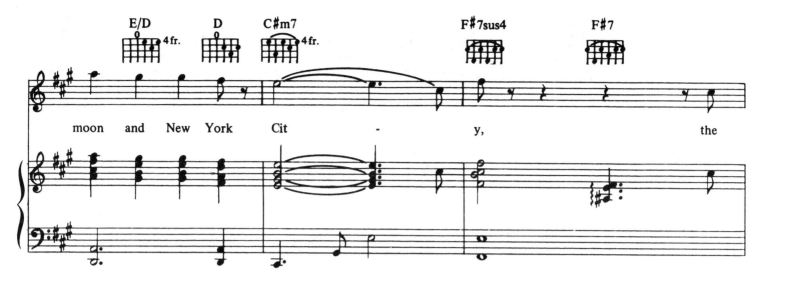

moon and New York Cit - y, the

best that you can do, the best that you can do

is fall in love.

Bright Eyes

Words & Music by Mike Batt

death down-stream   oh is it a dream?
hills un-seen   or is it a dream?

There's a fog a-long__ the hor - i - zon
There's a high__ wind__ in the trees __

a strange glow in __ the sky _____ and
a cold sound in __ the air _____ and

no-bo-dy seems __ to know where you go   and what does it
no-bo-dy ev-er knows when you go   and where do you

9

mean / start

Oh oh is it a dream?
oh oh in-to the dark.

CHORUS

Bright eyes _____ burn - ing ___ like ___ fire, _____

Bright ___ eyes _____ how can you close ___ and fail ___

How can the light ___ that burned ___ so bright-ly

What I Did For Love

Words by Edward Kleban
Music by Marvin Hamlisch

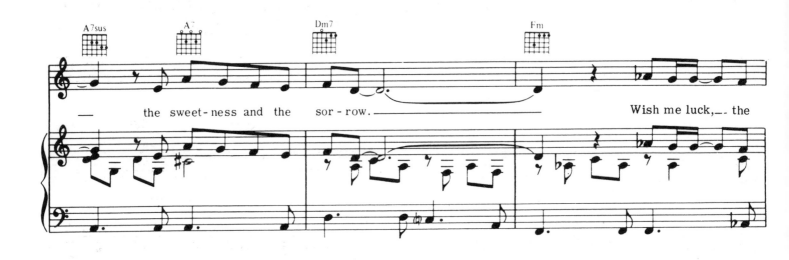

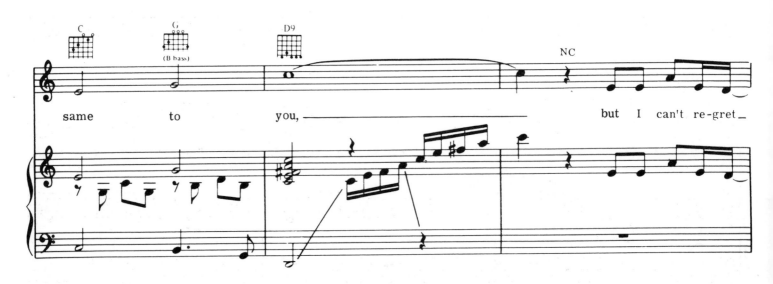

what I did for love, ____ what I did for ____ love. ____

Look, my eyes ____ are dry. _____ The gift was ours to

bor - row. _____ It's as if ____ we al - ways

knew, _____ and I won't for - get ____ what I did for love, —

Maria

Music by Leonard Bernstein
Lyrics by Stephen Sondheim

CHORUS
Moderately (warmly)

17

sud - den - ly I've found How won - der - ful a sound can be! Ma -

- ri - a! _____ Say it loud and there's mu - sic play - ing. Say it

soft and it's al - most like pray - ing. _____ Ma - ri - a, _____ I'll

Short version

nev - er stop say - ing, "Ma - ri - a". _____

18

Cabaret

Music by John Kander
Lyrics by Fred Ebb

cab - a - ret. _____ ret. Come taste the

wine, Come hear the band, Come blow the horn, start

cel - e - brat - ing, Right this way, your ta - ble's wait - ing. { No use per -
{ Start by ad -

mit - ting some proph - et of doom __ To wipe ev - 'ry smile a -
mit - ting from cra - dle to tomb _____ is - n't that long a

22

Sometimes

Words by Norman Newell
Music by Carl Davis

Some - times,— when things go wrong,

we try——. to un-der-stand   why—— the world stops

turn - ing —— and takes a - way—— the things we planned.   And

some - times____ we walk a - lone, no one____ ap - pears to care. Some - times____ we long for some - one____ to be the ans - wer____ to ev - 'ry prayer. When, through the mist of my tears I saw you, I knew I'd wait - ed

for you to find all the dreams____ that lost their way.

Who knows____ if we will win? God knows____ we wont give in;

There is____ no yes-ter-day now,____ there's just to - day now____ to find my

26

On Golden Pond
(Theme from)

Composed by Dave Grusin

Allegretto grazioso

Theme From E.T.
(The Extra-Terrestrial)

Composed by John Williams

Against All Odds
(Take A Look At Me Now)

Words & Music by Phil Collins

1. How can I just let you walk a-way, just let you leave with-out a trace? When I
(2. 3. see additional lyrics)

stand here tak - ing ev - 'ry breath with you;____ Ooh,____ You're the

on-ly one who real-ly knew me at all.____ So take a look at me now,—

2. How can you just walk away from me
   When all I can do is watch you leave?
   'Cause we shared the laughter and the pain,
   And even shared the tears.
   You're the only one who really knew me at all.

3. I wish I could just make you turn around,
   Turn around and see me cry.
   There's so much I need to say to you,
   So many reasons why.
   You're the only one who really knew me at all.

Theme From 'Gandhi'
(For All Mankind)

Composed by Ravi Shankar & George Fenton
Produced by George Fenton

1.2. *To next strain*

3.4.etc. *Repeat ad lib and fade*

41

One

Music by Marvin Hamlisch
Words by Edward Kleban

One singular sensation ev-'ry lit-tle step she takes,—

One thrill-ing com-bi-na-tion

Ev-'ry move that she makes. One smile and

sud-den-ly no-bod-y else will do, You know you'll

nev-er be lone-ly with you-know-who. One

mo-ment in her pres-ence and you can for-get the rest,

For the girl is sec-ond best ____ to none, son,

Summertime Blues

Words & Music by Eddie Cochran & Jerry Capehart

Fast Rock Beat

No chord

(Spoken:) Well, let's rock it now!

Well, I'm a - gon-na raise a fuss, I'm a - gon-na raise a hol - ler.

Mona Lisa

Words & Music by Jay Livingston & Ray Evans

Refrain Slowly Rubato

Mo - na Li - sa, Mo - na Li - sa men have named you: You're so

like the la - dy with the mys - tic smile. Is it on - ly 'cause you're lone - ly__ they have

blamed you for that Mo - na Li - sa strange-ness in your smile? Do you

smile to tempt a lov - er,__ Mo - na Li - sa,_____ Or is

Big Spender

Words by Dorothy Fields
Music by Cy Coleman

good time,_____ Let me show you a good time._____ The min-ute you

CODA

tacet
Hey, Big Spend-er!__

tacet
Hey, Big Spend-er!__

Spend_____ a lit-tle time_with me, Spend a lit-tle time_with

me, Spend a lit-tle time_with me._____

Rhapsody In Blue

Composed by George Gershwin

Moderately slow, with expression

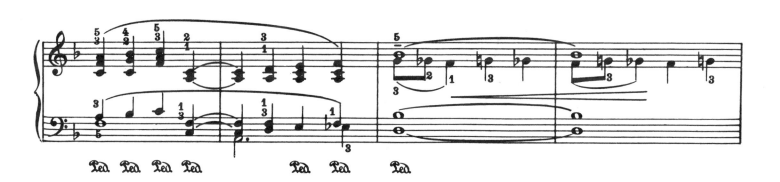

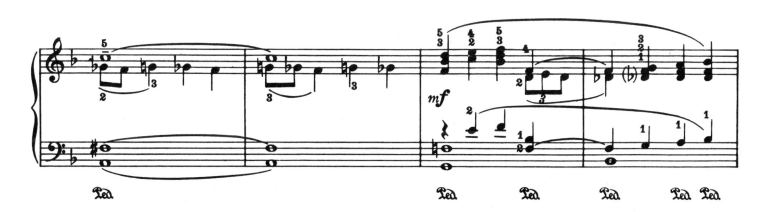

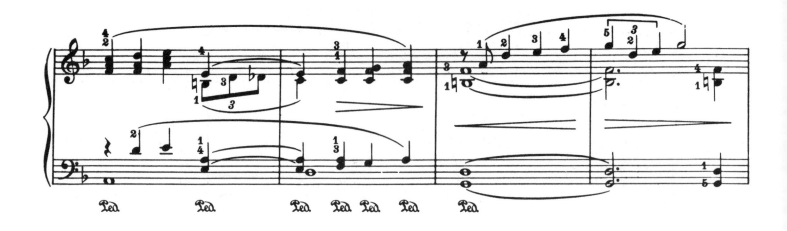

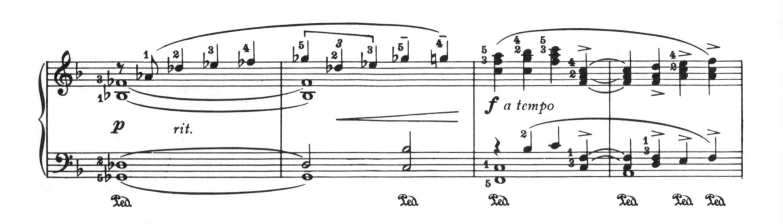

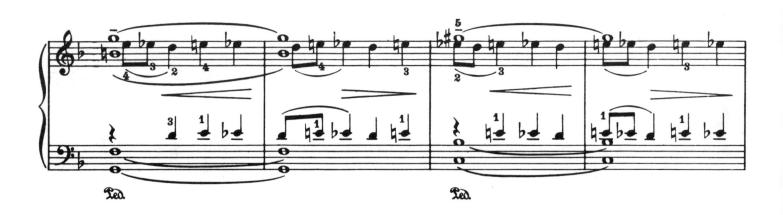

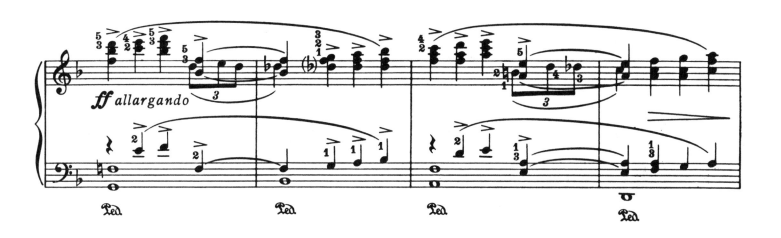

La Bamba

Adapted & Arranged by Ritchie Valens

Moderate "Latin Rock" beat

Tonight

Music by Leonard Bernstein
Lyrics by Stephen Sondheim

slow-ly And still the sky is light. _____ O

moon, grow bright, And make this end-less day end-less

night _____ to - night! _____ to -

- night! _____

The Power Of Love

Words & Music by Johnny Colla, Chris Hayes & Huey Lewis

bad girl's dream,_____ make a bad one_____ good_____ um_____ make a wrong one right,

power of love_____ that keeps you home at night.

CHORUS

You don't need mon - ey,
And it don't take mon - ey,

don't take fame;
don't take fame;

don't_____ need no cred - it card_____ to ride this train. It's
don't_____ need no cred - it card_____ to ride this train. It's

strong_____ and it's sud - den and it's cruel some - times,_____ but it might just save your life.
strong_____ and it's sud - den it can be cruel some - times,_____ but it might just save your

tacet

That's the pow - er of love, that's the pow - er of love._____

First time you feel_____ it, it might_____ make you sad._____ Next time you feel it it might_____

67

Star Wars (Main Theme)

By John Williams

March (Majestic)

Star Wars - 2 - 0

Evergreen

Words by Paul Williams
Music by Barbra Streisand

Moderately, with feeling

Ah.

Love,_____ soft as an eas-y chair;_____

The Entertainer

By Scott Joplin

Christine's Theme

Music by John Duprez

All The Way

Words by Sammy Cahn
Music by James Van Heusen

Eye Of The Tiger

Words & Music by Frankie Sullivan III & Jim Peterik

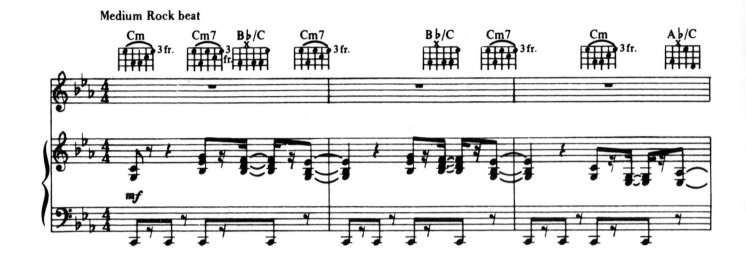

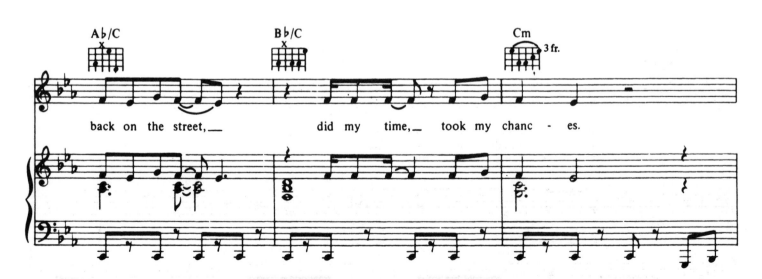

Went the dis - tance. Now I'm back on my feet, just a man ___ and his will to sur - vive. ___

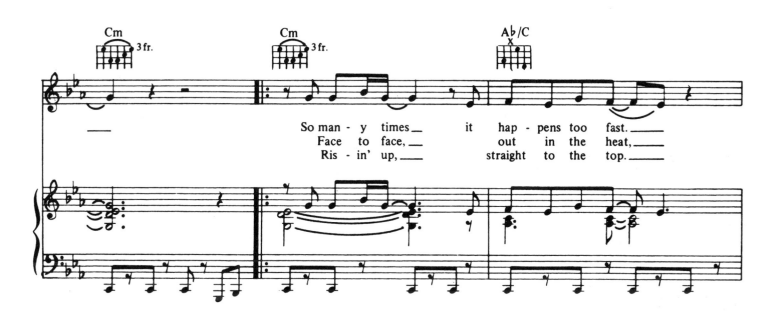

So man - y times ___ it hap - pens too fast. ___
Face to face, ___ out in the heat, ___
Ris - in' up, ___ straight to the top. ___

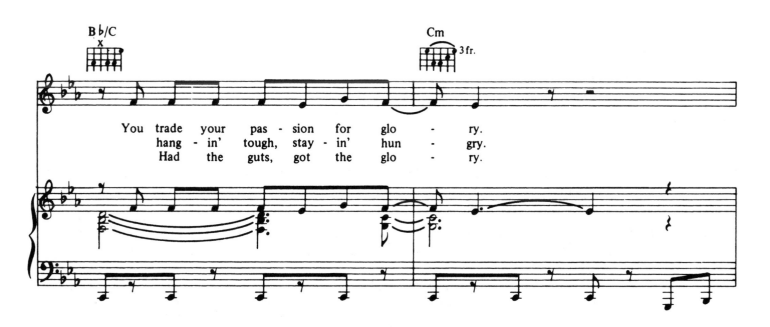

You trade your pas - sion for glo - ry.
hang - in' tough, stay - in' hun - gry.
Had the guts, got the glo - ry.

Don't lose your grip__ on the dreams of the past. You must
They stack the odds,__ still we take to the street for the
Went the dis - tance. Now I'm not gon - na stop, just a

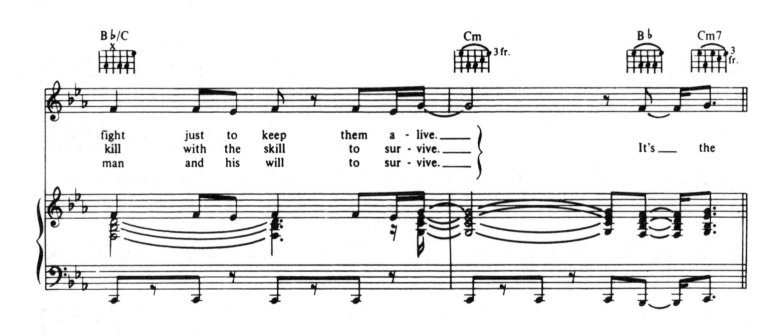

fight just to keep them a - live._____
kill with the skill to sur - vive._____
man and his will to sur - vive._____ It's ___ the

eye of the ti - ger. It's the thrill of the fight, ris - in'

up to the chal-lenge of our ri - val. And ___ the last known sur - vi - vor stalks his

prey in the night, and ___ he's watch - in' us all with the

eye   of the ti - ger.

eye _____   of the ti - ger.

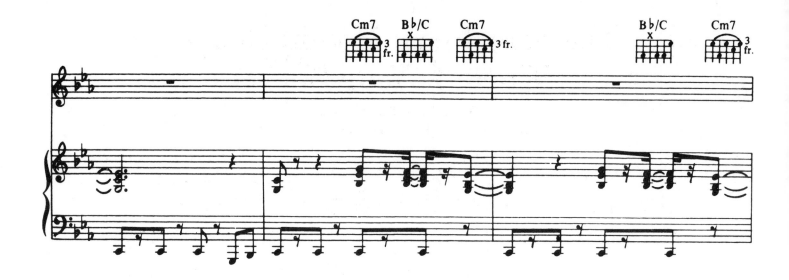

Repeat and fade

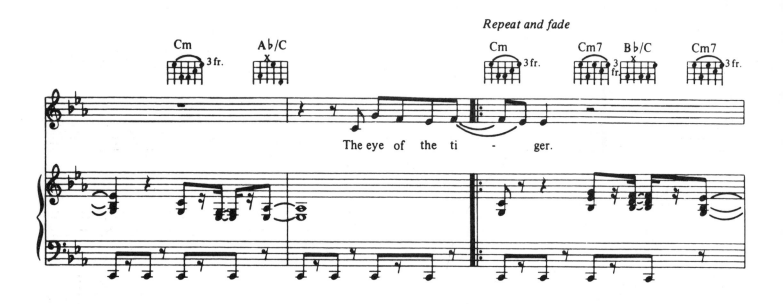

The eye of the ti - ger.

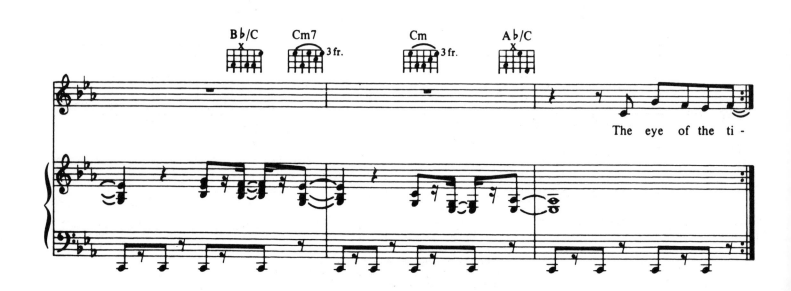

The eye of the ti -

90

The Song From Moulin Rouge
(Where Is Your Heart)

Words by William Engvick
Music by Georges Auric

eyes,   pre - tend - ing that I'm some - one else?   You

must   break the   spell,   this   cloud   that I'm

un - der.   So please   won't you   tell,   dar - ling,

where   is   your   heart?   When -   heart?

dim. e rall.

Pennies From Heaven

Words by John Burke
Music by Arthur Johnston

gain; that's what storms were made for and you should-n't be a-fraid, _____ For

REFRAIN *(a tempo)*

ev - 'ry time it rains, it rains pen - nies from hea - ven. ___

Don't you know each cloud con - tains

things you love, you must have show - ers. _____

So when you hear it thun - der, don't run un - der a tree, _____

_____ there'll be pen - nies from hea - ven for you and

1.
me.

2.
me. _____

Do You Know Where You're Going To?

Words by Gerry Goffin

Music by Michael Masser

Moderato – with expression

Do you know _____ where you're go-ing to? Do you like the things that life is show - ing you? _____ Where are you go - ing to, _____ do you know?

Now ____ look-ing back at all ____ we planned,

we let ____ so man - y dreams ____ just slip through our hands. ____

Why must_we wait so long_ be - fore we see

how sad the ans - wers to those ques - tions can be?_

know?

Coda

Chariots Of Fire

Composed by Vangelis

To Coda ◆

D.%. al Coda

⊕CODA

An American In Paris

Music by George Gershwin

Blues tempo
Andante ma con ritmo deciso

110

Everybody's Talkin'

Words & Music by Fred Neil

Falling In Love Again

Music & Original Words by Friedrich Hollander
English Words by Reg Connelly

From Here To Eternity

Words by Robert Wells
Music by Fred Karger

As Time Goes By

Words & Music by Herman Hupfeld

as time goes by. And

when two lov-ers woo, they still say "I love you," on that you can re-ly;____

____ no mat-ter what the fu-ture brings as time goes

by. Moon-light and love____ songs,

never out of date, hearts full of pas-sion, jeal-ous-y and hate;

wo-man needs man and man must have his mate, that no one can de-

ny. It's still the same old sto-ry, a fight for love and glo-ry, a

case of do or die._____ The world will al-ways wel-come

Strangers In The Night

Words by Charles Singleton & Eddie Snyder
Music by Bert Kaempfert

warm em-bracing dance a - way and ev- er since that night_____ we've been to - geth-er,

a tempo

Lov-ers at first sight,_____ In love for- ev - er, It turned out so right,_____

For strangers in the night._____

night._____

rit.